What to do when you can't learn the times tables

By
Steve Chinn

Egon Publishers Ltd
618 Leeds Road, Outwood, Wakefield, WF1 2LT

What to do when you can't learn the times tables

First Edition 1996
Second Edition 2009
Egon Publishers Ltd
618 Leeds Road, Outwood
Wakefield WF1 2LT

Tel/FAX: 01924 871697

www.egon.co.uk
information@egon.co.uk

ISBN: 978 1904160 95 3

There are 5 books in this series :-

What to do when you can't tell the time
What to do when you can't add and subtract
What to do when you can't multiply and divide
What to do when you can't do the times tables
What to do when you can't do fractions, decimals and percentages

Typeset by Omega Cottage DTP and Web Design
Tingley, Wakefield

CONTENTS

ABOUT THIS BOOK

This book is one of a series of books which have been written to make maths and numbers easier to remember, use and understand. The skills and the needs of learners who find maths difficult have been major influences in how these books are constructed. The books take a fresh look at maths skills, helping many more people to understand the patterns that make learning more successful.

This whole book, even if not a very big one, has been devoted to those basic facts which are known as 'the times tables'. There are many people who find that it is very difficult to retain these facts in their memories. They try hard to memorise them and may succeed, for a short while, but ultimately the facts do not stay in their memory. This leads to stress and sets the seeds that grow into a lack of confidence with maths and numbers.

This book offers an alternative approach to accessing these important facts. It is not a magic cure, nor a quick fix. It will involve effort and a lot of practice, but it does acknowledge that the facts that people can access are often restricted to 1x, 2x, 5x and 10x. It makes that into a strength. It explains how that is all you need to remember to work out the other facts and in doing so you will learn a lot about maths as well.

The same ideas and principles are used in all the 'What to do...' books. These ideas link together, building skills and understanding. Being unable to remember all the times table facts is not a problem, it can be changed into an advantage. After all, being able to remember them all does not automatically make you good at maths. Understanding will always beat recall.

Steve Chinn
February 1996 and April 2009

TWO WAYS TO WORK

This book is organised into an Introduction and three other Sections. Sections 1 and 2 offer the same basic ideas, but in a different order.

In Section 1, the times tables are taken in number groups, for example, all the 2x facts are covered together on pages 27 to 34.

In Section 2, each times table fact is dealt with separately. Some of the instructions from Section 1 may be repeated, but it allows you to dip into the book at a fact that you particularly need.

Remember, this is not a quick fix book. Each method will require practice and perseverance, but the learner will be left with a much better understanding of the facts and of numbers and of multiplication. When the memory fails, the learner has an alternative method. The all too frequent 'learned helplessness' of giving up is replaced by a positive alternative strategy.

You may find that as the learner becomes more familiar and at ease with the strategies that s/he starts to use only a part of the strategy, just enough to confirm an uncertain retrieval. For example, many people when asked for the answer to 7 x 5 are uncertain whether it is 30 or 35. One of the patterns for the 5x table facts is that any odd number times 5 gives an answer that ends in (that is, has a unit digit of) 5, and as 7 is odd, the answer is 35.

Section

1

THE TASK AHEAD

The times or multiplication facts are often presented in tables for a particular number. For example, the 2 x table is written:

$$0 \times 2 = 0$$
$$1 \times 2 = 2$$
$$2 \times 2 = 4$$
$$3 \times 2 = 6$$
$$4 \times 2 = 8$$
$$5 \times 2 = 10$$
$$6 \times 2 = 12$$
$$7 \times 2 = 14$$
$$8 \times 2 = 16$$
$$9 \times 2 = 18$$
$$10 \times 2 = 20$$

This can be an inefficient way to learn these basic multiplication facts. It does not show the links between different 'tables', for example, 3 x 2 is learned separately from 2 x 3.

This book works from the TIMES TABLE SQUARE which presents all the facts at one time and can also be used to show division facts and factors.

THE TIMES TABLE SQUARE

	0	1	2	3	4	5	6	7	8	9	10
0	0	0	0	0	0	0	0	0	0	0	0
1	0	1	2	3	4	5	6	7	8	9	10
2	0	2	4	6	8	10	12	14	16	18	20
3	0	3	6	9	12	15	18	21	24	27	30
4	0	4	8	12	16	20	24	28	32	36	40
5	0	5	10	15	20	25	30	35	40	45	50
6	0	6	12	18	24	30	36	42	48	54	60
7	0	7	14	21	28	35	42	49	56	63	70
8	0	8	16	24	32	40	48	56	64	72	80
9	0	9	18	27	36	45	54	63	72	81	90
10	0	10	20	30	40	50	60	70	80	90	100

At the back of this book in Section Three, there are four blank grids. The blank grids can be used to keep a record of progress.

These grids maybe photocopied. Knowing how to complete the times table square is one of the goals of this book.

USING THE TIMES TABLE SQUARE

	0	1	2	3	4	5	6	7	8	9	10
0	0	0	0	0	0	0	0	0	0	0	0
1	0	1	2	3	4	5	6	7	8	9	10
2	0	2	4	6	8	10	12	14	16	18	20
3	0	3	6	9	12	15	18	21	24	27	30
4	0	4	8	12	16	20	24	28	32	36	40
5	0	5	10	15	20	25	30	35	40	45	50
6	0	6	12	18	24	30	36	42	48	54	60
7	0	7	14	21	28	35	42	49	56	63	70
8	0	8	16	24	32	40	48	56	64	72	80
9	0	9	18	27	36	45	54	63	72	81	90
10	0	10	20	30	40	50	60	70	80	90	100

In the Times Table Square the facts are given twice, once across the table in the rows, and again down the table in columns.

To find the answer to a fact, for example 5 x 7:

Find 5 in the top row.
Run your finger down the 5x column until it meets 7x row.
Where the 5 column and the 7 row cross is the answer, 35.

HOW TO HALVE THE TASK

The Square has 121 facts to learn.

This number can be reduced to almost half by recognising a symmetry in the numbers in the square. This symmetry is a result of a mathematical link between facts.

The order in which you multiply two numbers does not matter, the answer will be the same.

For example,

$$6 \times 4 = 24 \quad \text{and} \quad 4 \times 6 = 24$$
$$7 \times 9 = 63 \quad \text{and} \quad 9 \times 7 = 63$$

You can demonstrate this link by using 24 coins, (or counters, or cubes).

4 rows of 6   are the same as   6 rows of 4

4 x 6   is the same as   6 x 4

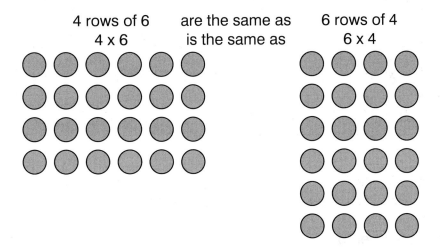

We can generalise this link as:

number A x number B = number B x number A

This is known as the **commutative property**.

The presentation of the link could be shortened even further to

A x B = B x A (and that is algebra!)

	0	1	2	3	4	5	6	7	8	9	10
0	0	0	0	0	0	0	0	0	0	0	0
1	0	1	2	3	4	5	6	7	8	9	10
2	0	2	4	6	8	10	12	14	16	18	**20**
3	0	3	6	9	**12**	15	18	21	24	27	30
4	0	4	8	**12**	16	20	24	**28**	32	36	40
5	0	5	10	15	20	25	30	35	40	45	50
6	0	6	12	18	24	30	36	42	48	54	60
7	0	7	14	21	**28**	35	42	49	56	**63**	70
8	0	8	16	24	32	40	48	56	64	72	80
9	0	9	18	27	36	45	54	**63**	72	81	90
10	0	10	**20**	30	40	50	60	70	80	90	100

The symmetry in the Times Table Square is across the diagonal. Five pairs of numbers have been **highlighted** to illustrate the symmetry. 52 facts are duplicated, so for example, if you know that 4 x 7 = 28 then you know that:

7 x 4 is also 28

The numbers on the diagonal are known as 'squares'. The two numbers multiplying each other are the same. If the numbers represented the sides of a rectangle, that shape would be a square, as for example with 3 x 3:

The square facts are:

1 x 1   2 x 2   3 x 3   4 x 4   5 x 5
6 x 6   7 x 7   8 x 8   9 x 9   10 x 10

WORDS USED FOR X

MULTIPLY   6 multiply by 5 = 30

TIMES   6 times 5 = 30

PRODUCT   30 is the product of 6 x 5

LOTS OF   6 lots of 5 = 30

OF $\frac{1}{5}$ of 30 = 6

Sometimes, no word at all, as in 'six sevens' or 'three nines'.

Examples:

- Multiply 3 by 5
- Seven times four is twenty-eight
- What is the product of 10 and 6?
- What are nine eights?
- What are four lots of five?
- A quarter of twelve (¼ x 12)

WHAT IS MULTIPLICATION?

The standard definition of multiplication is that it is *repeated addition*. What that means is:

adding the same number repeatedly, for example:

$$8 + 8 + 8 + 8 + 8 \quad \text{is} \quad 5 \text{ lots of } 8 \quad \text{or} \quad 5 \times 8$$

and

$$3 + 3 + 3 + 3 + 3 + 3 + 3 + 3 + 3 + 3$$
$$\text{is ten lots of } 3 \quad \text{or} \quad 10 \times 3$$

Multiplication and addition are closely linked. We shall be combining this link with the concept of repeated addition to help you access all the times table facts by using a few **key facts**.

GETTING A PICTURE

For many people the times table facts have no reality. Children learn them by rote, sometimes to music. They often fail to see any patterns, links or significance in the facts. They may not even have any sense of the relative values of the numbers involved. They may see nine as 9, an isolated, unconnected, abstract symbol. They may not see 9 as 1 less than 10. These problems carry through into adulthood.

One of the ways learning can be made more memorable is to create pictures and images. Another way is to let the learner handle objects to create a kinaesthetic memory (similar to remembering the spatial pattern on the key pad for a familiar phone number). Some teachers use simple equipment such as counters or coins to demonstrate an idea. This book suggests some ideas. Not all learners will relate to materials, but many will.

There are some squares and number strips at the back of this book. They can be photocopied onto card and then cut out. They can be coloured in. Check if they help the learner to understand the strategies. They will not help all learners. Some may prefer to use coins.

The squares have an advantage in that they introduce the image of area as a way of understanding number A x number B. This image will be useful in later maths topics such as 'long' multiplication and even algebra.

It is one of the unique features of the 'What to do...' books that the same idea is developed from basics to the seemingly complex.

Using the squares

The squares can be used to show the link between 'lots of' and area as ways of picturing multiplication.

Make a line of 4 squares: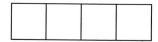

This is 'one lot of 4'. It is also an area of 1 x 4.

Make two lines:

  2 x 4

This is 'two lots of 4'. It is also an area of 2 x 4.

This arrangement of 8 squares could be turned through 90° to demonstrate that 2 x 4 has the same answer as 4 x 2.
(see also page 7)

  Number A x Number B   =   Number B x Number A

  4 x 2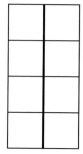

STARTING THE TASK

When the task ahead of you seems very difficult, especially if you have tried before, maybe many times, then it can be very hard to get started. What you will be able to do now is to make some very quick (and relatively easy) progress.

Also it is worth keeping the Number A x Number B = Number B x Number A in mind as it almost halves the task.

The biggest number in the Table Square is 100. In order to develop some sense of number values it is worth comparing other times table answers to 100. For example:

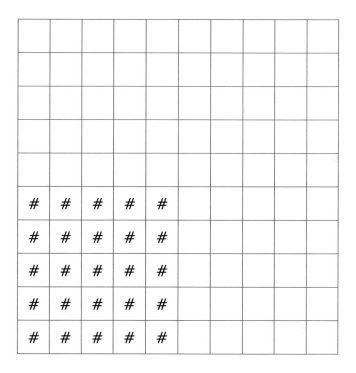

5 x 5 = 25
25 is one quarter of 100.

$7 \times 7 = 49$

50 is half of 100.

$1 \times 10 = 10$

10 is one tenth of 100.

SOME QUICK PROGRESS

The Table Square shows 121 facts.

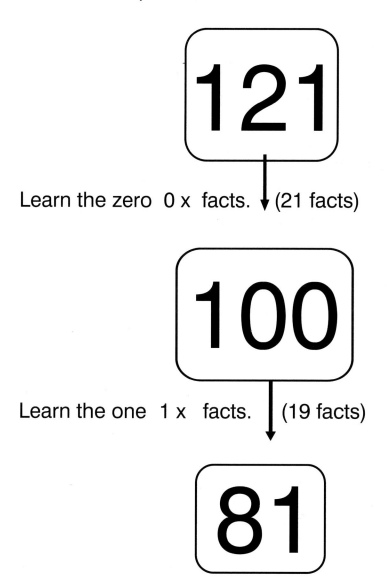

Learn the zero 0 x facts. ↓ (21 facts)

Learn the one 1 x   facts. (19 facts)

Note: The zero and the one facts are a little exceptional and do not set a pattern for the other numbers.

0   zero   *0*

nothing

0   **nil**   *0*

none

nought

Zero   0

The answers to the zero times tables are easy to remember, because:

THEY ARE ALL ZERO

When ANY number is multiplied by zero the answer is always zero.
For example:

$$2 \times 0 = 0$$

and   1 billion x zero = 0

or   1 000 000 000 x 0 = 0

This outcome is more obvious if we use 'lots of' for 'multiply'.
2 x 0 is '2 lots of zero' which must still be zero.
Two lots of nothing are still nothing.

1000 000 000 x 0 is 'one billion lots of zero' which still is zero.
No matter how many 'lots of' zero we have, the answer is still zero.

The same applies when the order is reversed:

$$0 \times 2 = 0$$

and:

zero times 1 billion = 0

0 x 1000 000 000 = 0

Zero lots of two must be zero.

Zero lots of a billion must still be zero.

You have learned 21 facts.

100 to go!

0	0	0	0	0	0	0	0	0	0	0
0										
0										
0										
0										
0										
0										
0										
0										
0										
0										

1 ONE

 1p

unit   1

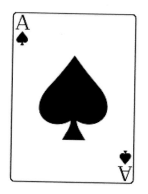

Single

ONE   1

The answers to the 1 x table are the same value as the multiplying number. For example,   1 x 5 = 5   1 x 8 = 8

One 'lot of' any number must be the same as that number, for example, one lot of 4 must be 4.

The 1 x table has a simple pattern:

1 x 1 =	1		1 x 1 =	1
2 x 1 =	2		1 x 2 =	2
3 x 1 =	3		1 x 3 =	3
4 x 1 =	4		1 x 4 =	4
5 x 1 =	5		1 x 5 =	5
6 x 1 =	6		1 x 6 =	6
7 x 1 =	7		1 x 7 =	7
8 x 1 =	8		1 x 8 =	8
9 x 1 =	9		1 x 9 =	9
10 x 1 =	10		1 x 10 =	10

As with all the times table facts, the order of multiplying does not change the answer. So:

$$1 \times 9 = 9 \times 1 = 9$$

and $$1 \times 5 = 5 \times 1 = 5$$

1 lot of 5 = 5

5 lots of 1 = 5

0	0	0	0	0	0	0	0	0	0	0
0	1	2	3	4	5	6	7	8	9	10
0	2									
0	3									
0	4									
0	5									
0	6									
0	7									
0	8									
0	9									
0	10									

The 1x facts give you
19 new facts on the table square.

81 to go!

10 Ten

decade

 **10**

decimal

0 10 20 30 40 50

60 70 80 90 100

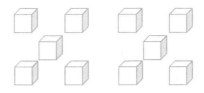

10   2 x 5 = 10

TEN   10

There is a pattern for the answers and the pattern is related to the number which is multiplied by 10.

For example: 4 x 10 = 40
                    9 x 10 = 90

This pattern is in the digits. In terms of place value, a unit digit becomes a tens digit.

It is also a verbal pattern:

Ten times four is forty
Ten times nine is ninety

Our number system is based on 10, which makes it a key number. The place values of numbers are in multiples of ten, for example:

Tens	unit x 10
Hundreds	ten x 10
Thousands	hundred x 10

Our number system is based on 10 because we have 10 fingers.

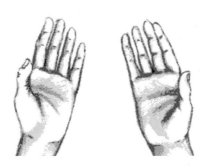

```
 0 x  10 =   0          10 x  0 =    0
 1 x  10 =  10          10 x  1 =   10
 2 x  10 =  20          10 x  2 =   20
 3 x  10 =  30          10 x  3 =   30
 4 x  10 =  40          10 x  4 =   40
 5 x  10 =  50          10 x  5 =   50
 6 x  10 =  60          10 x  6 =   60
 7 x  10 =  70          10 x  7 =   70
 8 x  10 =  80          10 x  8 =   80
 9 x  10 =  90          10 x  9 =   90
10 x  10 = 100          10 x 10 =  100
```

Ten is the first two digit number: 1 2 3 4 5 6 7 8 9 **10**

The 0 tells us there are no units and the 1, written to the left of the zero, tells us there is one ten.

So,   20, twenty, is two tens: 2 lots of 10

        30, thirty, is three tens: 3 lots of 10

        40, forty, is four tens: 4 lots of 10

and this pattern continues up to

        90, ninety, is nine tens: 9 lots of 10

When we reach ten tens, 10 lots of 10, we move to a three digit number:

        100, one hundred

Coins or base ten blocks can be used to provide images

Ten 1p coins	=	one 10p coin
10 x 1p	=	1 x 10p

Ten 10p coins	=	one pound (100p) coin
10 x 10p	=	1 x £1 = 1 x 100

Base ten blocks:

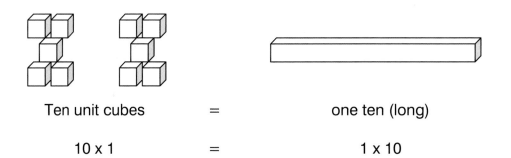

Ten unit cubes	=	one ten (long)
10 x 1	=	1 x 10

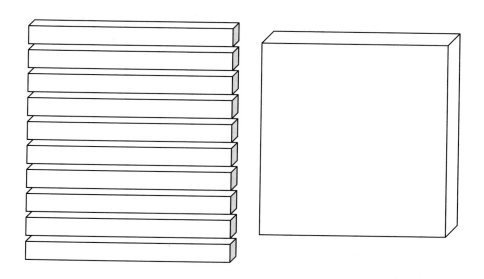

| Ten tens (longs) | = | one hundred (flat) |
| 10 x 10 | = | 1 x 100 |

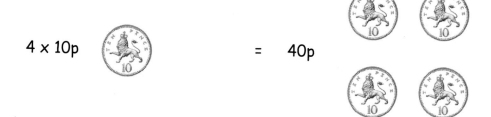

4 x 10p   =   40p

25

The pattern of words/sounds for the ten times tables

The ten times table is the only one from 2x to 10x where the question virtually tells you the answer. This is down to the word links:

- **One** times ten is ten
- **Two** times ten is twenty   (two-ty)
- **Three** times ten is thirty (three-ty)
- **Four** times ten is forty (four-ty)
- **Five** times ten is fifty   (five –ty)
- **Six** times ten is sixty
- **Seven** times ten is seventy
- **Eight** times ten is eighty
- **Nine** times ten is ninety
- **Ten** times ten is one hundred (The pattern ends here!)

The ten times table
has given you 17 extra facts.

64 to go!

(and don't forget that we can almost halve that 64,
because A x B = B x A.)

0	0	0	0	0	0	0	0	0	0	0
0	1	2	3	4	5	6	7	8	9	10
0	2									20
0	3									30
0	4									40
0	5									50
0	6									60
0	7									70
0	8									80
0	9									90
0	10	20	30	40	50	60	70	80	90	100

The 10 x facts are key facts, so it is important to learn them as we will use them to work out many other facts and to answer many other number problems.

The other key facts are the 1x, the 2x and the 5x facts.

TWO   2

pair

twice

BI·CYCLE

duet

twin

2

dual

0 2 4 6 8 10 12 14 16 18 20

couple

II

TWO 2

The two times facts are KEY FACTS. They can be used to work out many more facts and number problems.

The pattern for the 2x answers is a pattern of even numbers. Even numbers are numbers that can be divided into two equal whole number parts. For example,

6 is an even number and can be divided into two lots of 3:

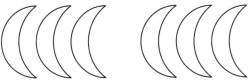

7 is not an even number (it is an odd number) and cannot be divided into two equal whole number parts,

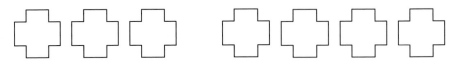

The first five even numbers set the pattern for all the other even numbers:

2   4   6   8   10

The next five even numbers are: 12 14 16 18 20

and the next are: 22 24 26 28 30

and then: 32 34 36 38 40 etc.

*Even numbers always have as their unit digit **2** or **4** or **6** or **8** or **0**. If any* *whole number is multiplied by 2, it will become an even number. All the answers in the 2x table are even numbers.*

0 x 2 =	0		2 x 0 =	0
1 x 2 =	2		2 x 1 =	2
2 x 2 =	4		2 x 2 =	4
3 x 2 =	6		2 x 3 =	6
4 x 2 =	8		2 x 4 =	8
5 x 2 =	10		2 x 5 =	10
6 x 2 =	12		2 x 6 =	12
7 x 2 =	14		2 x 7 =	14
8 x 2 =	16		2 x 8 =	16
9 x 2 =	18		2 x 9 =	18
10 x 2 =	20		2 x 10 =	20

Accessing the 2x answers by counting up in twos

A lot of children, and probably quite a few adults who think they 'know' the 2x table can only give an answer by counting up in twos, often counting using their fingers. For example, if asked 'what is 7 x 2?' they count up using 7 fingers:

2   4   6   8   10   12   **14**

A way to shorten the counting

Counting on for the facts from 1 x 2 to 5 x 2 is acceptable if it is reasonably quick. Most people can recall 5 x 2 = 10.

5 x 2 is a useful half-way point. It uses all the fingers on one hand and 5 x 2 equals 10. To count that, it would be the even number pattern of:

2   4   6   8   10

6 x 2 is 5 x 2 plus 1 x 2
      (one hand of twos and one extra finger of two)

7 x 2 is 5 x 2 plus 2 x 2
      (one hand of twos and two extra fingers of two)

8 x 2 is 5 x 2 plus 3 x 2
      (one hand of twos and three extra fingers of two)

9 x 2 is 5 x 2 plus 4 x 2
      (one hand of twos and four extra fingers of two)

The 2x table can be written in two halves to show this recurring pattern:

0 x 2 = 0	5 x 2 = 10
1 x 2 = 2	6 x 2 = 12
2 x 2 = 4	7 x 2 = 14
3 x 2 = 6	8 x 2 = 16
4 x 2 = 8	9 x 2 = 18

This could be demonstrated with 2p coins:

1 x 2 = **2**

2 x 2 = **4**

3 x 2 = **6**

4 x 2 = **8**

5 x 2 = **10**

At this stage, the five 2p coins
can be traded, or exchanged,
for one 10p coin and the pattern
of extra 2p coins will repeat itself,
but with a 10p coin in each stage.

The 10p coin represents 5 x 2 = 10

6 x 2   =   **12**   **(10 + 2)**

7 x 2   =   **14**   **(10 + 4)**

8 x 2   =   **16**   **(10 + 6)**

9 x 2   =   **18**   **(10 + 8)**

The same demonstration could be done with the base ten 'unit cubes' and the 'ten longs'.

So, if you were using fingers for 7 x 2.

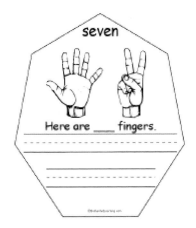

The first hand with its 5 fingers represents 10 and you need 2 fingers on the second hand to go from 5 to 7.

Those two fingers are 2 x 2 = 4, so 10 + 4 = 14 or 7 x 2 = 14

To talk your way through that process:

Seven times two is five times two plus two times two, 5 x 2 is 10, then add on 2 x 2 is 4, 10 plus 4 gives 14.

To write it in maths symbols:

$$7 \times 2 = \quad 5 \times 2 \quad + \quad 2 \times 2$$
$$7 \times 2 = \quad\quad 10 \quad + \quad\quad 4 \quad = 14$$

The two times table has given you 15 new facts.

49 to go!

0	0	0	0	0	0	0	0	0	0	0
0	1	2	3	4	5	6	7	8	9	10
0	2	4	6	8	10	12	14	16	18	20
0	3	6								30
0	4	8								40
0	5	10								50
0	6	12								60
0	7	14								70
0	8	16								80
0	9	18								90
0	10	20	30	40	50	60	70	80	90	100

FIVE   5

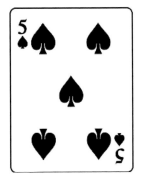

pentagon

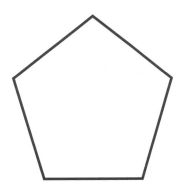

0 5 10 15 20 25 30 35 40 45 50

####

quintuplets

V

$$10 \div 2 = 5$$

FIVE   5

The 5x facts are part of the KEY FACTS. If you can learn just these key facts, then you can use them to work out all the other times table facts, and much more!

The key facts are: 1x   2x   5x   10x

A useful link between the 5x facts and the 10x facts:

five is half of 10, $5 = 10 \div 2$

This means that the 5x facts can be worked out by halving the 10x facts.

This rule applies to any number times 5, for example:

$$82 \times 5$$

$82 \times 10 = 820$ so $82 \times 5 = 820 \div 2 = 410$

The 5x table compared to the 10x table answers.

The 10x answers are in green.

	5x	10x			5x	10x
0 x 5 =	0	0	5 x	0 =	0	0
1 x 5 =	5	10	5 x	1 =	5	10
2 x 5 =	10	20	5 x	2 =	10	20
3 x 5 =	15	30	5 x	3 =	15	30
4 x 5 =	20	40	5 x	4 =	20	40
5 x 5 =	25	50	5 x	5 =	25	50
6 x 5 =	30	60	5 x	6 =	30	60
7 x 5 =	35	70	5 x	7 =	35	70
8 x 5 =	40	80	5 x	8 =	40	80
9 x 5 =	45	90	5 x	9 =	45	90
10 x 5 =	50	100	5 x	10 =	50	100

Using coins to illustrate the relationship between the 10x and the 5x tables

Use 5p and 10p coins to explore the relationship, for example, set up 3 of the 5p coins and 3 of the 10p coins and compare the total value of each group.

       3 x 10p = 30p

       3 x 5p = 15p

The three 5p coins are worth half of the three 10p coins.

Set up another comparison:

        8 x 10p = 80p

        8 x 5p = 40p

Another pattern

0 x 5 =   0
1 x 5 =   5
2 x 5 = 10
3 x 5 = 15
4 x 5 = 20   Look at the unit digit in each answer.
5 x 5 = 25
6 x 5 = 30
7 x 5 = 35   As you move down the answers, the unit digit
8 x 5 = 40   alternates between 0 and 5.
9 x 5 = 45
10 x 5 = 50

(2, 4, 6, 8 and 10 are even numbers, check back in the 2x tables if you have forgotten this concept.)

1, 3, 5, 7 and 9 are odd numbers.

If you multiply 5 by an even number, the answer will be a multiple of 10.

If you multiply 5 by an odd number, the answer will have 5 in the unit place.

The reason is that even numbers (lots of) of 5 pair up to make 10, but. odd numbers (lots of) of fives have one 5 left over from any pairing.

Look at these examples which use 5p coins.
First an even number, 6:

$$6 \times 5p = 30p$$

Now an odd number of 5p coins, 9:

$$9 \times 5p = 45p$$

8 of the 9 coins pair up to make 40p. One 5p coin is left to make 45p.

Working out a 5x answer from a 10x answer

You halve the 10x answer to get the 5x answer:

For example,   To find 8 x 5:

$$8 \times 10 = 80 \qquad\qquad 8 \times 5 \text{ must be half of } 80$$
$$80 \div 2 = 40, \text{ so } 8 \times 5 = 40$$

(Check that even numbers x 5 have 0 in the unit place of the answer.)

To find 7 x 5:

$$7 \times 10 = 70 \qquad\qquad 7 \times 5 \text{ must be half of } 70,$$
$$70 \div 2 = 35 \quad \text{ so, } 7 \times 5 = 35$$

(Check that odd numbers x 5 have 5 in the unit place of the answer.)

This strategy works for any number x 5.

For example,   5 x 41 = half of 410 = 205

The five times table has given you 13 new facts.

36 to go!

0	0	0	0	0	0	0	0	0	0	0
0	1	2	3	4	5	6	7	8	9	10
0	2	4	6	8	10	12	14	16	18	20
0	3	6			15					30
0	4	8			20					40
0	5	10	15	20	25	30	35	40	45	50
0	6	12			30					60
0	7	14			35					70
0	8	16			40					80
0	9	18			45					90
0	10	20	30	40	50	60	70	80	90	100

You now have all the key facts that you need to memorise. If you can remember these facts, you can use them to complete the times table square by simple combinations of two relevant facts.

There is a very powerful way of rote learning, but, like many good ideas, it will not work for everyone.

Most of us tend to rote learn more effectively if we hear the information in OUR OWN VOICES.
Self-voice learning can be stunningly effective and is based on research done by Steve Chinn with Dr Colin Lane.
("Google" ARROW to update on Dr Lane's work)

SELF-VOICE LEARNING

Select the information you want to memorise, for example, the 2x table facts. Record the facts, with time gaps between each separate fact, onto an audio machine or onto a computer.

Take one fact and continually repeat the play-back of the information, preferably through headphones, as you look at the fact.

Learning then becomes multi-sensory.

You can see the information on paper or on the screen.

You can hear the information from play-back in your own voice.

You can voice the information, even if it is only sub-vocalising.

This is a method to use in short bursts, concentrating on a few items of information. You will notice its efficacy, or not, quite soon after first use.

It is so important to master the key facts of 1x, 2x, 5x and 10x, that this method is well worth a trial.

USING THE KEY FACTS

The key facts of 1x, 2x, 5x and 10x can be used to work out all the other facts and many more maths problems including division and multiplication with all numbers (big and small!).

There is a link here to money. Have you noticed that our coins and notes use the key values:

1p, 2p, 5p, 10p, 20p, 50p, £1, £2, £5 (note), £10 (note).

To calculate times table facts

Any times table fact can be calculated by combining two of the key
facts. This strategy avoids the situation so well expressed by a 12 year
old girl,

*'I don't get stuck in other subjects – only maths. When I'm doing
English, I can always get on with my work. If I'm not sure about a
spelling, I can just have a go and still get my work done. But I can't
do that in maths. If I'm stuck I can't do anything but wait for help.'*

The links are:

Adding links: 3 = 2 + 1

6 = 5 + 1

7 = 5 + 2

Subtracting link: 9 = 10 – 1

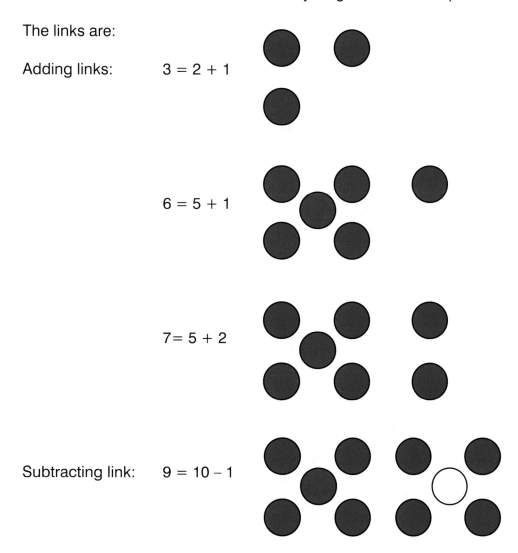

Multiplying link: 4 = 2 x 2

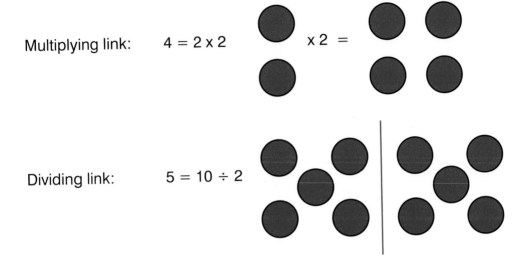

Dividing link: 5 = 10 ÷ 2

The principle behind these links is used for more advanced calculations and algebra. Learning how to use these strategies will set the foundations for many further topics in maths.

We can start by looking at the multiplying strategy and the 4x table.

FOUR   4

$2 \times 2 = 4$ $2^2 = 4$

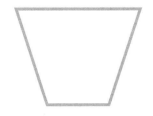

quadrilateral

IV

0 4 8 12 16 20 24 28 32 36 40

quad bike

Quadruple

FOUR   4

The strategy for working out the 4x facts is to multiply by 2, twice.
The link is:

$$2 \times 2 = 4$$

For example, to work out   **7 x 4**

The two steps are: $7 \times 2 = 14$
$14 \times 2 = 28$

7 x 4 = 28

The 4x table is written out below with the 2x answers in green next to
the linked 4x answers.

	4x	2x			4x	2x
0 x 4 =	0	0		4 x 0 =	0	0
1 x 4 =	4	2		4 x 1 =	4	2
2 x 4 =	8	4		4 x 2 =	8	4
3 x 4 =	12	6		4 x 3 =	12	6
4 x 4 =	16	8		4 x 4 =	16	8
5 x 4 =	20	10		4 x 5 =	20	10
6 x 4 =	24	12		4 x 6 =	24	12
7 x 4 =	28	14		4 x 7 =	28	14
8 x 4 =	32	16		4 x 8 =	32	16
9 x 4 =	36	18		4 x 9 =	36	18
10 x 4 =	40	20		4 x 10 =	40	20

This 'double doubling' can be demonstrated with unit cubes or coins

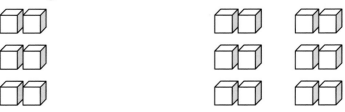

$2 \times 3 = 6$ $2 \times 6 = 12$

so, $3 \times 4 = 12$

Odd fact:

If you re-write the 3 x 4 = 12 fact as 12 = 3 x 4, then the digits are in numerical order: 1 2 3 4

The only other example of digits in order in the table square is:

for 7 x 8 = 56, or

56 = 7 x 8   5 6 7 8

When practising these facts it may be helpful to vocalise the process.

Another idea is to have the 2x and the 4x facts on flash cards and match them.

The 4x facts give you 11 new facts.

only 25 to go!!

In the square below the 2x and the 4x facts across the square have been printed in **green** to highlight the 2 x 2 = 4 link.

0	0	0	0	0	0	0	0	0	0	0
0	1	2	3	4	5	6	7	8	9	10
0	2	4	6	8	10	12	14	16	18	20
0	3	6		12	15					30
0	4	8	12	16	20	24	28	32	36	40
0	5	10	15	20	25	30	35	40	45	50
0	6	12		24	30					60
0	7	14		28	35					70
0	8	16		32	40					80
0	9	18		36	45					90
0	10	20	30	40	50	60	70	80	90	100

NINE　　9

9

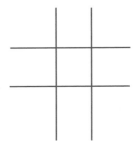

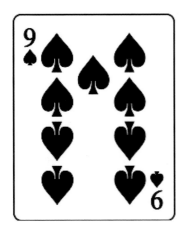

IX

0　9　18　27　36　45　54　63　72　81　90

3 x 3

3^2　　　　10 - 1

NINE   9

The 9x facts can be accessed by using the 10x facts.

This strategy also introduces the useful skill of estimation.

There is a simple way to check the answers for the 9x table facts.

The 9x facts have several patterns which will help you to access them if you cannot retrieve them from memory.

Nine and ten

Nine is the number before ten.

Nine is one less than ten.

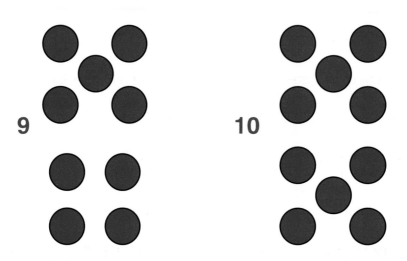

$$9 = 10 - 1$$

You can use your (ten) fingers to show this relationship. You could count up, one by one, to show 9 fingers, or you could hold up 10 fingers and then fold 1 finger down, leaving 9 fingers.

Ten is an easy number to work with. It is often easier to round up a 9 value to a 10, do the maths with the tens, and then readjust to the exact answer.

For example, to add six nines: 9 + 9 + 9 + 9 + 9 + 9

First add six tens: 10 + 10 + 10 + 10 + 10 + 10 = 60

Each of the six tens was one more than the nine,

     so take away 6 from 60: 60 − 6 =

     to get the answer for adding six nines: 54

An example from maths in everyday life:

Many items in shops are priced at £1.99, £4.99 or £9.99 and so on.

If you have to add £1.99 + £2.99 + £9.99.

Round up each amount to: £2 + £3 + £10
(N.B. You have added 1p to each of the three prices: 3p)

Add the rounded amounts: £15, this is the *estimate*.

Now take back (subtract) the 3p: £15 − 3p = £14.97, this is the **exact** answer.

The key link is: **9 is 1 less than 10**

The pattern for the 9x table

The pattern of the link to the 10x table can be demonstrated with the strips at the end of this book. They can be photocopied onto card and cut up. The diagrams following also illustrate the link.

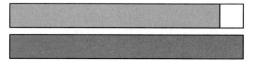

One nine is one less than one ten.

$$1 \times 9 \ = \ 1 \times 10 \ - \ 1 \times 1$$

Two nines are two less than two tens.

$$2 \times 9 \ = \ 2 \times 10 \ - \ 2 \times 1$$

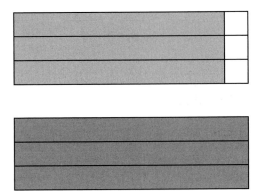

Three nines are three less than three tens.

$$3 \times 9 \quad = \quad 3 \times 10 \quad - \quad 3 \times 1$$

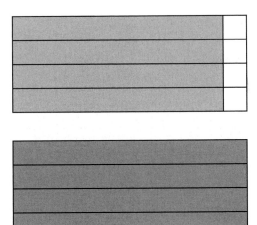

Four nines are four less than four tens.

$$4 \times 9 \quad = \quad 4 \times 10 \quad - \quad 4 \times 1$$

The pattern continues. So, if we had to work out 23 x 9, we can use the pattern:

Twenty-three nines are twenty-three less than twenty-three tens.

$$23 \times 9 \quad = \quad 23 \times 10 - 23 \times 1$$

$$23 \times 9 \quad = \quad 230 - 23 = 207$$

The 9x table is set out below with the relationship to the 10x facts set out in green.

9x			9x	10x
0 x 9 = 0	0		9 x 0 = 0	0
1 x 9 = 9	10 - 1		9 x 1 = 9	10 - 1
2 x 9 = 18	20 - 2		9 x 2 = 18	20 - 2
3 x 9 = 27	30 - 3		9 x 3 = 27	30 - 3
4 x 9 = 36	40 - 4		9 x 4 = 36	40 - 4
5 x 9 = 45	50 - 5		9 x 5 = 45	50 - 5
6 x 9 = 54	60 - 6		9 x 6 = 54	60 - 6
7 x 9 = 63	70 - 7		9 x 7 = 63	70 - 7
8 x 9 = 72	80 - 8		9 x 8 = 72	80 - 8
9 x 9 = 81	90 - 9		9 x 9 = 81	90 - 9
10 x 9 = 90	100 - 10		9 x 10 = 90	100 - 10

A pattern for checking answers

The digits of every answer in the 9x table add up to 9.

$$0 + 9 = 9$$
$$1 + 8 = 9$$
$$2 + 7 = 9$$
$$3 + 6 = 9$$
$$4 + 5 = 9$$
$$5 + 4 = 9$$
$$6 + 3 = 9$$
$$7 + 2 = 9$$
$$8 + 1 = 9$$
$$9 + 0 = 9$$

This rule applies to the answer of **ANY number multiplied by 9**.

We worked out 23 x 9 on page 58. The answer was 207.

$$2 + 0 + 7 = 9$$

Try some 9x multiplications on a calculator and add up the digits in the answers.

Another idea

If you don't like taking away the 'ones' when working out the 9x table facts, try using the 'adds up to 9' rule and the 10x estimation:

For example,

6 x 9 is less than 7 x 10.
7 x 10 is 70,
so 7 x 9 is going to be sixty something, where the 'something' (□) is the units digit.
So 7 x 9 = 6□. From the 'adds up to 9' pattern:
$$6 + \square = 9$$
□ must be 3, so the answer is 63.

The 9x facts give you nine new facts.

Only 16 left!

0	0	0	0	0	0	0	0	0	0	0
0	1	2	3	4	5	6	7	8	9	10
0	2	4	6	8	10	12	14	16	18	20
0	3	6		12	15				27	30
0	4	8	12	16	20	24	28	32	36	40
0	5	10	15	20	25	30	35	40	45	50
0	6	12		24	30				54	60
0	7	14		28	35				63	70
0	8	16		32	40				72	80
0	9	18	27	36	45	54	63	72	81	90
0	10	20	30	40	50	60	70	80	90	100

There is another way of accessing the 9x facts, known as the 'finger' or 'gypsy' method. This is explained on page 73.

THREE 3   SIX 6   SEVEN 7   EIGHT 8

triangle

3

HEXAGON

6

Monday, Tuesday, Wednesday, Thursday, Friday, Saturday, Sunday

Septagon

7

octagon

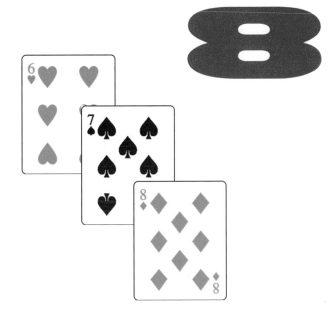

octopus

THREE 3   SIX 6   SEVEN 7

The 3x 6x and 7x facts can be worked out by the same process.

The process breaks down the numbers 3, 6 and 7 into key numbers:

$$
\begin{aligned}
3 \quad &\text{as} \quad 2 + 1 \\
6 \quad &\text{as} \quad 5 + 1 \\
7 \quad &\text{as} \quad 5 + 2
\end{aligned}
$$

It also uses the 'lots of' way of picturing the multiplication.
For example:

3 x 6 is 3 lots of 6

3 x 6 is worked out as:

'2 lots of 6' plus '1 lot of 6' equals '3 lots of 6'.

$$3 \times 6 \quad = \quad 2 \times 6 \quad + \quad 1 \times 6 \quad = \quad 12 + 6 = 18$$

6 x 6 is 6 lots of 6

6 x 6 is worked out as:

'5 lots of 6' plus '1 lot of 6' equals '6 lots of 6'.

$$6 \times 6 \quad = \quad 5 \times 6 \quad + \quad 1 \times 6 \quad = \quad 30 + 6 \quad = \quad 36$$

7 x 6 is 7 lots of 6

It is worked out as:

'5 lots of 6' plus '2 lots of 6' equals '7 lots of 6'.

$$7 \times 6 \quad = \quad 5 \times 6 \quad + \quad 2 \times 6 \quad = \quad 30 + 12 \quad = \quad 42$$

This breaking down strategy is used in mathematics for complex multiplications. For example, to multiply 321 x 67 by the traditional method, the computation will be done in two steps, two 'lots of' and then the two 'lots of' are added together:

$$
\begin{array}{rr}
321 \times 60 = & 19260 \\
321 \times\ \ 7 = & 2247 \\
\hline
321 \times 67 = & 21507
\end{array}
$$

The 3x facts

If we look at the remaining 3x facts on the table square:

0	0	0	0	0	0	0	0	0	0	0
0	1	2	3	4	5	6	7	8	9	10
0	2	4	6	8	10	12	14	16	18	20
0	3	6	?	12	15	?	?	?	27	30
0	4	8	12	16	20	24	28	32	36	40
0	5	10	15	20	25	30	35	40	45	50
0	6	12	?	24	30				54	60
0	7	14	?	28	35				63	70
0	8	16	?	32	40				72	80
0	9	18	27	36	45	54	63	72	81	90
0	10	20	30	40	50	60	70	80	90	100

These are: 3 x 3,   6 x 3,   7 x 3,   8 x 3.

3 x 3 is the familiar 9 square used in noughts and crosses:

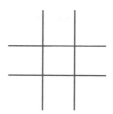

$$3 \times 3 = 9$$

6 x 3 is '6 lots of 3', which is '5 lots of 3' plus '1 lot of 3'.

6 x 3	=	5 x 3	+	1 x 3	
	=	15	+	3	= **18**

7 x 3 is '7 lots of 3', which is '5 lots of 3' plus '2 lots of 3'.

7 x 3	=	5 x 3	+	2 x 3	
	=	15	+	6	= **21**

8 x 3 is '8 lots of 3', which is '8lots of 3' plus '3 lots of 3'.

8 x 3	=	5 x 3	+	3 x 3	
	=	15	+	9	= **24**

Alternatively you could consider 8 x 3 as 3 x 8, 3 lots of 8

3 x 8 is '3 lots of 8' which is '2 lots of 8' plus '1 lot of 8'.

3 x 8	=	2 x 8	+	1 x 8	
	=	16	+	8	= **24**

Add these facts to the times table square and it now looks like this:

0	0	0	0	0	0	0	0	0	0	0
0	1	2	3	4	5	6	7	8	9	10
0	2	4	6	8	10	12	14	16	18	20
0	3	6	**9**	12	15	**18**	**21**	**24**	27	30
0	4	8	12	16	20	24	28	32	36	40
0	5	10	15	20	25	30	35	40	45	50
0	6	12	**18**	24	30				54	60
0	7	14	**21**	28	35				63	70
0	8	16	**24**	32	40				72	80
0	9	18	27	36	45	54	63	72	81	90
0	10	20	30	40	50	60	70	80	90	100

There are just 9 facts to go!!!!

The 6x facts

The remaining facts in the 6x table are: 6 x 6, 7 x 6, and 8 x 6.

We shall use the 'lots of' method.

6 x 6 is '6 lots of 6' which is '5 lots of 6' plus '1 lot of 6'.

6 x 6	=	5 x 6	+	1 x 6		
	=	30	+	6	=	**36**

7 x 6 is '7 lots of 6' which is '5 lots of 6' plus '2 lots of 6'.

7 x 6	=	5 x 6	+	2 x 6		
	=	30	+	12	=	**42**

8 x 6 will be worked out as 6 x 8 below.

The 7x facts

The remaining facts of the 7x table are: 7 x 7 and 8 x 7.

7 x 7 is '7 lots of 7' which is '5 lots of 7' plus '2 lots of 7'.

7 x 7	=	5 x 7	+	2 x 7		
	=	35	+	14	=	**49**

8 x 7 will be worked out as 7 x 8 below.

The 8x facts

The remaining facts are: 6 x 8, 7 x 8 and 8 x 8.

6 x 8 is '6 lots of 8' which is '5 lots of 8' plus '1 lot of 8'.

6 x 8	=	5 x 8	+	1 x 8
	=	40	+	8 = **48**

7 x 8 is '7 lots of 8' which is '5 lots of 8' plus '2 lots of 8'.

7 x 8	=	5 x 8	+	2 x 8
	=	40	+	16 = **56**

Note: If 7 x 8 = 56 is re-written as   56 = 7 x 8

then the digits are in numerical order, 5 6 7 8!

8 x 8 is accessed by repeated multiplication by 2:

$$2 \times 2 \times 2 = 8$$

So: 2 x 2 x 2 x 2 x 2 x 2

$$
\begin{aligned}
\mathbf{2} \times \mathbf{2} &= 4 \\
4 \times \mathbf{2} &= 8 \\
8 \times \mathbf{2} &= 16 \\
16 \times \mathbf{2} &= 32 \\
32 \times \mathbf{2} &= 64
\end{aligned}
$$

2   4   8   16   32   64

The last fact: 8 x 8 = 64

The times table square is completed.

0	0	0	0	0	0	0	0	0	0	0
0	1	2	3	4	5	6	7	8	9	10
0	2	4	6	8	10	12	14	16	18	20
0	3	6	9	12	15	18	21	24	27	30
0	4	8	12	16	20	24	28	32	36	40
0	5	10	15	20	25	30	35	40	45	50
0	6	12	18	24	30	36	42	48	54	60
0	7	14	21	28	35	42	49	56	63	70
0	8	16	24	32	40	48	56	64	72	80
0	9	18	27	36	45	54	63	72	81	90
0	10	20	30	40	50	60	70	80	90	100

A useful strategy for examinations

Sometimes the pressure and anxiety felt in exams makes it even harder to remember facts. It is unlikely that you will be allowed to take a times table square into an examination, but it is likely that you will be allowed to have squared paper. If so, then you could try this idea:

Draw up this key facts only square. You should be able to do this quite quickly. Then when you need a particular fact, work out just that fact.

0	0	0	0	0	0	0	0	0	0	0
0	1	2	3	4	5	6	7	8	9	10
0	2	4	6	8	10	12	14	16	18	20
0	3	6			15					30
0	4	8			20					40
0	5	10	15	20	25	30	35	40	45	50
0	6	12			30					60
0	7	14			35		49			70
0	8	16			40					80
0	9	18			45					90
0	10	20	30	40	50	60	70	80	90	100

For example, if the fact is 7 x 7:

Use 2 x 7 plus 5 x 7, **14 + 35** and fill in the 7 x 7 square with **49**.

Odd fact 1

A link for the squared numbers:

3 x 3   4 x 4   5 x 5   6 x 6   7 x 7   8 x 8   9 x 9

Take the number above and the number below the squared number and multiply, for example with 4 x 4, this would lead to 3 x 5 (the 'each side' numbers).

The answer will always be 1 less than the answer to the square:

3 x 3 = 9	4 x 2 = 8
4 x 4 = 16	5 x 3 = 15
5 x 5 = 25	6 x 4 = 24
6 x 6 = 36	7 x 5 = 35
7 x 7 = 49	8 x 6 = 48
8 x 8 = 64	9 x 7 = 63
9 x 9 = 81	10 x 8 = 80

The 4 x 4 square shows how this works:
To convert the 4 x 4 to 5 x 3, the three grey squares are moved, leaving the green square for the +1 in: 5 x 3 + 1 = 16.

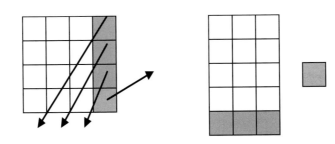

Odd fact 2

Another link for the squared numbers

The squared numbers follow a sequence. Look at the pattern of differences (subtractions) between each successive number.

0 x 0 = 0		
1 x 1 = 1	1 – 0 = 1	
2 x 2 = 4	4 – 1 = 3	
3 x 3 = 9	9 – 4 = 5	
4 x 4 = 16	16 – 9 = 7	
5 x 5 = 25	25 – 16 = 9	
6 x 6 = 36	36 – 25 = 11	
7 x 7 = 49	49 – 36 = 13	
8 x 8 = 64	64 – 49 = 15	
9 x 9 = 81	81 – 64 = 17	
10 x 0 = 100	100 – 81 = 19	It is a sequence of odd numbers.

We can demonstrate the link by using squares.

To move up from 3 x 3 to 4 x 4 we add 3 squares to two sides:

3 x 3

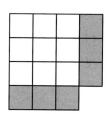

Then we add one extra square to make the odd number 3 + 3 + 1 = 7

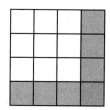

Odd fact 3

The 'gypsy' method for the 9x facts

Example: 3 x 9

Place all 10 fingers on the edge of a table (remember that, for maths, thumbs count as fingers). Tuck in the 3rd finger from the left.

This leaves 2 fingers to the left of the tucked in finger and 7 fingers to the right, giving an answer:

$$3 \times 9 = 27$$

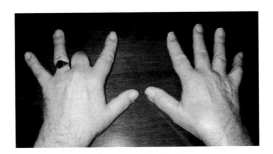

Try for 6 x 9:

Tuck in the 6th finger from the left.

This leaves 5 fingers to the left of the tucked in finger and 4 fingers to the right, giving an answer:

$$6 \times 9 = 54$$

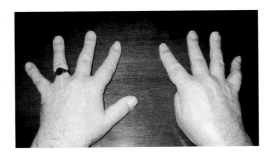

What to do when you can't learn the times tables

Section

2

Section 2. Individual times table facts

In Section 2, each times table fact from 3x to 9x is dealt with separately.

EXCEPT, each 'reverse' or commutative fact. These will be included in the heading.

So, for example, if you want to look up 7 x 3,
you may have to look for 3 x 7.

The 0x, 1x, 2x and 10x facts are not included in this section.

When you look up a fact, such as 7 x 3, there will be an explanation of how to use the key facts of   1x,   2x,   5x,   and   10x, to work out the answer.

At the end of this book are some key number fact cards.

When you look up a fact, such as 7 x 3, there will be an explanation of how to use the key number fact cards of   1x,   2x,   5x,   and   10x, to work out the answer.

3 x 3 = 9

3 x 3 is a square, 3^2

Key numbers: 3 = 2 + 1

'3 times 3' can be written as '3 lots of 3', which can then be done in two parts:

Step 1:   2 lots of 3 = 2 x 3 = 6
Step 2:   1 lot of 3 = 1 x 3 = 3   and add the two parts together.
Add   3 lots of 3 = 3 x 3 = 9

Using the key number fact cards:

$$2 \text{ x } 3 = 6$$

+

$$1 \text{ x } 3 = 3$$

(6 + 3 = 9)

3 x 3 = 9

4 x 3 = 12   **(also 3 x 4 = 12)**

     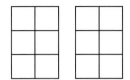

2 x 3 = 6   2 x 6 = 12

The key numbers are: 2 x 2 = 4

4x is worked out by using 2x twice:

Step 1.   2 x 3 = 6
Step 2:   2 x 6 = 12   so, 4 x 3 = 12

Using the key number fact cards:

Select the key 2x card and double the answer on the card.

$$2 \times 3 = 6$$

(2 x 6 = 12)

4 x 3 = 12

5 x 3 = 15   (also 3 x 5 = 15)

The two steps here use the link between 10 and 5.

The key numbers are: $10 \div 2 = 5$

It follows from this that:

'5 lots of 3' = '10 lots of 3' divided by 2.

Step 1: $10 \times 3 = 30$
Step 2: $30 \div 2 = 15$

            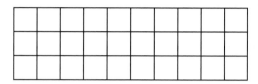

1 x 3   10 x 3 = 30

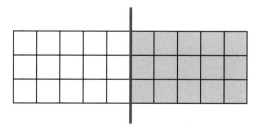

30 ÷ 2 = 15

Using the key number fact cards:

Chose the 10x key number fact card and half the answer.

10 x 3 = 30

(30 ÷ 2 = 15)

5 x 3 = 15

6 x 3 = 18   **(also 3 x 6 = 18)**

6 splits into key numbers 5 and 1: $6 = 5 + 1$.

     '6 lots of 3' = '5 lots of 3' + '1 lot of 3'.

Step 1:	5 x 3 = 15
Step 2:	1 x 3 = 3
Add:	6 x 3 = 18

Using the key number fact cards:

$$5 \ x \ 3 = 15$$

$$+$$

$$1 \ x \ 3 \ = \ 3$$

(15 + 3 = 18)

6 x 3 = 18

7 x 3 = 21   (also 3 x 7 = 21)

7 splits into key numbers 5 and 2: $7 = 5 + 2$.

'7 lots of 3' = '5 lots of 3' + '2 lots of 3'.

Step 1:	5 x 3 = 15
Step 2:	2 x 3 = 6
Add:	7 x 3 = 21

Using the key number fact cards:

Select the two key number fact cards (5 x 3 and 2 x 3) and add the answers.

5 x 3 = 15

+

2 x 3 = 6

(15 + 6 = 21)

7 x 3 = 21

8 x 3 = 24   (also 3 x 8 = 24)

Method 1

Based on the key numbers: $8 = 2 \times 2 \times 2$.

 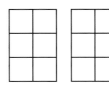 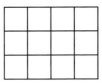 

2 x 3 = 6   2 x 6 = 12   2 x 12 = 24

8 x 3 is worked out by using 2x three times:

Step 1.   2 x 3 =   6
Step 2:   2 x   6 = 12
Step 3:   2 x 12 = 24

Method 2

Take 8 x 3 and turn it around into 3 x 8, '3 lots of 8':

'3 lots of 8' = '2 lots of 8' + '1 lot of 8'

Step 1:   2 x 8 = 16
Step 2:   1 x 8 =   8
Add: 3 x 8 = 24

Using the key number fact cards:

Select the key 2x card (2 x 3) and double the answer on the card, twice.

$$2 \text{ x } 3 = 6$$

(4 x 3 = 12)

8 x 3 = 24

$$9 \times 3 = 27 \qquad \text{(also } 3 \times 9 = 27\text{)}$$

9 splits into key numbers: 10 and 1 (note the subtraction), $9 = 10 - 1$

'9 lots of 3' = '10 lots of 3' – '1 lot of 3'

Step 1: $10 \times 3 = 30$
Step 2: $\underline{1 \times 3 = \ \ 3}$
Subtract: $9 \times 3 = 27$

Using the key number fact cards:

$$\boxed{10 \ \times \ 3 = 30}$$

$$-\qquad\qquad \textbf{(subtract)}$$

$$\boxed{1 \ \times \ 3 \ = \ 3}$$

$$(30 - 3 = 27)$$

$$\mathbf{9 \ \times \ 3 = \ 27}$$

First, don't forget,

Check for 9x facts: the digits in the answer add up to 9.

$$9 \times 3 = 27 \qquad 2 + 7 = 9$$

Second, don't forget,

You can use the gypsy (finger) method for any 9 x fact.

$$\mathbf{9 \times 3 \ = 27}$$

85

4 x 4 = 16

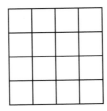

4 x 4 is a square, 4^2

Key numbers: 4 = 2 x 2

4 x 4 is worked out by multiplying by 2 twice.

Step 1:   2 x 4 = 8

Step 2:   2 x 8 = 16

Using the key number fact cards:

$$2 \times 4 = 8$$

(2 x 8 = 16)

4 x 4 = 16

5 x 4 = 20   (also 4 x 5 = 20)

The two steps here use the link between 10 and 5.

The key numbers are: $10 \div 2 = 5$

It follows from this that:

'5 lots of 4' = '10 lots of 4' divided by 2

Step 1:   10 x 4 = 40

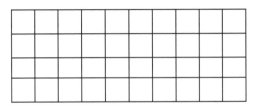

10 x 4 = 40

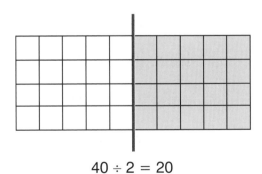

40 ÷ 2 = 20

Using the key number fact cards:

Chose the 10x key number fact card and half the answer.

$$10 \times 4 = 40$$

$$(40 \div 2 = 20)$$

$$5 \times 4 = 20$$

6 x 4 = 24   **(also 4 x 6 = 24)**

6 splits into key numbers: 5 and 1, $6 = 5 + 1$

      '6 lots of 4' = '5 lots of 4' + '1 lot of 4'.

Step 1:   5 x 4 = 20
Step 2:   <u>1 x 4 =   4</u>
Add: 6 x 4 = 24

Using the key number fact cards:

$$5 \ x \ 4 = 20$$

+

$$1 \ x \ 4 \ = \ 4$$

(20 + 4 = 24)

6 x 4 = 24

7 x 4 = 28   **(also 4 x 7 = 28)**

7 splits into key numbers: 5 and 2, $7 = 5 + 2$.

'7 lots of 4' = 5 lots of 4' + '2 lots of 4'.

Step 1:   5 x 4 = 20
Step 2:   2 x 4 = 8
Add: 7 x 4 = 28

Using the key number fact cards:

Select the two key number fact cards (5 x 4 and 2 x 4) and add the answers.

$$5 \times 4 = 20$$

$$+$$

$$2 \times 4 = 8$$

(20 + 8 = 28)

7 x 4 = 28

8 x 4 = 32   (also 4 x 8 = 32)

Method 1

Based on the key numbers: 8 = 2 x 2 x 2

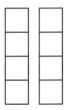
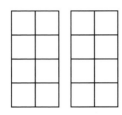
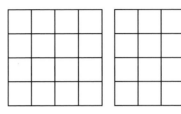

2 x 4 = 8   2 x 8 = 16   2 x 16 = 32

8 x 4 is worked out by using 2x three times:

Step 1:   2 x 4 =   8
Step 2:   2 x 8 = 16
Step 3:   2 x 16 = 32

Method 2

Take 8 x 4 and turn it around into 4 x 8, using 2x twice.

Step 1:   8 x 2 = 16
Step 2:   16 x 2 = 32

Using the key number fact cards:

Select the key 2x card (2 x 4) and double the answer on the card, twice.

$$2 \times 4 = 8$$

$$8 \times 2 = 16$$

$$16 \times 2 = 32$$

$$\mathbf{8 \times 4 = 32}$$

$$9 \times 4 = 36 \qquad \text{(also } 4 \times 9 = 36\text{)}$$

9 splits into key numbers: 10 and 1 (note the subtraction), $9 = 10 - 1$.

'9 lots of 4' = '10 lots of 4' - '1 lot of 4'.

Step 1: $10 \times 4 = 40$
Step 2: $\underline{1 \times 4 = 4}$
Subtract: $9 \times 4 = 36$

Using the key number fact cards:

10 x 4 = 40

-   **(subtract)**

1 x 4 = 4

$(40 - 4 = 40)$

$$9 \times 4 = 36$$

First, don't forget,

Check for 9x facts: the digits in the answer add up to 9.

$$9 \times 4 = 27 \qquad 3 + 6 = 9$$

Second, don't forget,

You can use the gypsy (finger) method for any 9x fact.

93

5 x 5 = 25

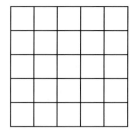

5 x 5 is a square, 5^2

Key numbers: $5 = 10 \div 2.$

5 x 5 is worked out by multiplying 5 by 10 and then dividing by 2.

Step 1:   10 x 5 = 50
Step 2:   50 ÷ 2 = 25

Using the key number fact cards:

$$10 \times 5 = 50$$

$$50 \div 2 = 25$$

25 is one quarter of 100. The reason that 5 x 5 gives a quarter of 100 is that both fives are a half of ten and a half times a half gives a quarter
$$\frac{1}{2} \times \frac{1}{2} = \frac{1}{4}$$

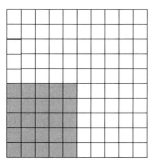

5 x 5 = 25

94

$$6 \times 5 = 30 \qquad \textbf{(also } 5 \times 6 = 30\textbf{)}$$

Method 1

6 splits into key numbers: 5 and 1, $6 = 5 + 1$.

'6 lots of 5' = '5 lots of 5' + '1 lot of 5'.

Step 1: $5 \times 5 = 25$
Step 2: $\underline{1 \times 5 = 5}$
Add: $6 \times 5 = 30$

Using the key number fact cards:

$$5 \times 5 = 25$$

$$+$$

$$1 \times 5 = 5$$

$$(25 + 5 = 30)$$

$$\mathbf{6 \ x \ 5 \ = \ 30}$$

Method 2

Key numbers: $5 = 10 \div 2$

6 x 5 is worked out by multiplying 6 by 10 and then dividing by 2.

Step 1: $6 \times 10 = 60$
Step 2: $60 \div 2 = 30$

$$\mathbf{6 \ x \ 5 = 30}$$

$$7 \times 5 = 35 \qquad \text{(also } 5 \times 7 = 35\text{)}$$

Method 1

7 splits into key numbers: 5 and 2, $7 = 5 + 2$

'7 lots of 5' =   '5 lots of 5' + '2 lots of 5'

Step 1:	$5 \times 5 = 25$
Step 2:	$\underline{2 \times 5 = 10}$
Add:	$7 \times 5 = 35$

Remember: Any odd number times 5 has a 5 in the unit place of the answer.

Using the key number fact cards:

Select the two key number fact cards (5 x 5 and 2 x 5) and add the answers.

$$5 \times 5 = 25$$

$$+$$

$$2 \times 5 = 10$$

$$(25 + 10 = 35)$$

$$\mathbf{7 \times 5 = 35}$$

Method 2

Key numbers: $10 \div 2$

7 x 5 is worked out by multiplying 7 by 10 and then dividing by 2.

Step 1:   7 x 10 = 70
Step 2:   70 ÷ 2 = 35

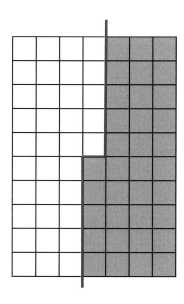

7 x 5 = 35

Note: Odd numbers x 5 have 5 in the unit place.

$$8 \times 5 = 40 \qquad \text{(also } 5 \times 8 = 40\text{)}$$

Method 1

8 splits into key numbers: 5 and 3, $8 = 5 + 3$

'8 lots of 5' =   '5 lots of 5' + '3 lots of 5'.

Step 1: $5 \times 5 = 25$
Step 2: $\underline{3 \times 5 = 15}$
Add: $8 \times 5 = 40$

Remember: Any even number times 5 has a 0 in the unit place of the answer.

Using the key number fact cards:

Select the two key number fact cards (5 x 5 and 3 x 5) and add the answers.

$$5 \times 5 = 25$$

$$+$$

$$3 \times 5 = 15$$

$$(25 + 15 = 40)$$

$$\mathbf{8 \times 5 = 40}$$

Method 2

Key numbers: $5 = 10 \div 2$

8×5 is worked out by multiplying 8 by 10 and then dividing by 2.

Step 1: $8 \times 10 = 80$
Step 2: $80 \div 2 = 40$

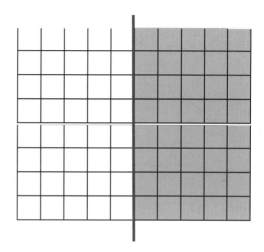

Note: Any even number times 5 has a 0 in the unit place of the answer.

Using the key number fact cards:

Select the key number fact card and divide the answer by 2.

$$8 \times 10 = 80$$

$(80 \div 2 = 40)$

$8 \times 5 = 40$

$$9 \times 5 = 45 \qquad \textbf{(also 5 x 9 = 45)}$$

9 splits into key numbers: 10 and 1, (note the subtraction): $9 = 10 - 1$

'9 lots of 5' = '10 lots of 5' - '1 lot of 5'.

Step 1: $10 \times 5 = 50$
Step 2: $\underline{1 \times 5 = 5}$
Subtract: $9 \times 5 = 45$

Using the key number fact cards:

$$10 \times 5 = 50$$

$$-$$ **(subtract)**

$$1 \times 5 = 5$$

$(50 - 5 = 50)$

$$9 \times 5 = 45$$

First, don't forget,

Check for 9x facts: the digits in the answer add up to 9.

$$9 \times 5 = 45 \qquad 4 + 5 = 9$$

Second, don't forget,

You can use the gypsy (finger) method for any 9x fact.

6 x 6

6 x 6 is a square, 6^2

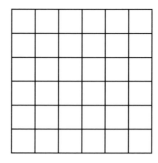

6 splits into key numbers: 5 and 1, $6 = 5 + 1$

'6 lots of 6' = '5 lots of 6' + '1 lot of 6'.

Step 1:   5 x 6 = 30
Step 2:   <u>1 x 6 =   6</u>
Add: 6 x 6 = 36

Using the key number fact cards:

$$5 \times 6 = 30$$

$$+$$

$$1 \times 6 = 6$$

(30 + 6 = 36)

6 x 6 = 36

$$7 \times 6 = 42 \qquad \text{(also } 6 \times 7 = 42\text{)}$$

7 splits into key numbers: 5 and 2, $7 = 5 + 2$

> '7 lots of 6' = '5 lots of 6' + '2 lots of 6'.

Step 1: $5 \times 6 = 30$
Step 2: $\underline{2 \times 6 = 12}$
Add: $7 \times 6 = 42$

Using the key number fact cards:

Select the two key number fact cards (5 x 6 and 2 x 6) and add the answers.

$$5 \times 6 = 30$$

$$+$$

$$2 \times 6 = 12$$

$$(30 + 12 = 42)$$

$$\mathbf{7 \ x \ 6 \ = \ 42}$$

(Another link: 7 x 6 has an answer that is twice that for 7 x 3 = 21 since 6 is 2 x 3.)

$$\mathbf{7 \times 6 = 42}$$

8 x 6 = 48   (also 6 x 8 = 48)

Method 1

Based on the key numbers: 8 = 2 x 2 x 2

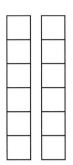 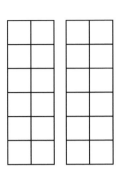 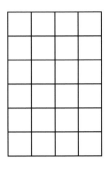 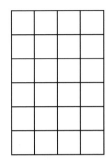

2 x 6 = 12   2 x 12 = 24   2 x 24 = 48

8 x 6 is worked out by using 2x three times:

Step 1.   2 x 6   = 12
Step 2:   2 x 12   = 24
Step 3:   2 x 24   = 48

Method 2

Take 8 x 6 and turn it around into 6 x 8,

        using '6 lots of 8' = '5 lots of 8' + '1 lot of 8'

Step 1:   5 x 8 = 40
Step 2:   1 x 8 =   8
Add: 6 x 8 = 48

Using the key number fact cards:

$$5 \times 8 = 40$$

$$+$$

$$1 \times 8 = 8$$

$(40 + 8 = 48)$

6 x 8 = 48

8 x 6 = 48

$$9 \times 6 = 54 \qquad \text{(also } 6 \times 9 = 54\text{)}$$

9 splits into key numbers: 10 and 1, (note the subtraction): $9 = 10 - 1$

'9 lots of 6' = '10 lots of 6' - '1 lot of 6'.

Step 1:	$10 \times 6 =$	60
Step 2:	$1 \times 6 =$	6
Subtract:	$9 \times 6 =$	54

Using the key number fact cards:

$$10 \times 6 = 60$$

$-$ **(subtract)**

$$1 \times 6 = 6$$

$(60 - 6 = 54)$

$$9 \ \times \ 6 \ = \ 54$$

First, don't forget,

Check for 9x facts: the digits in the answer add up to 9.

$$9 \times 6 = 54 \qquad 5 + 4 = 9$$

Second, don't forget,

You can use the gypsy (finger) method for any 9x fact.

7 x 7 = 49

7 x 7 is a square, 7^2

Compare 7 x 7 with 10 x 10.

10 x 10 = 100

7 x 7 = 49

7 x 7 is 1 less than 50.

50 is half of 100.

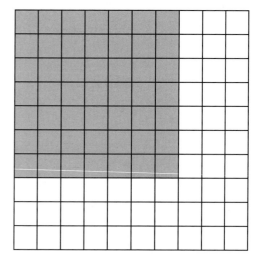

7 splits into key numbers: 5 and 2, 7 = 5 + 2

'7 lots of 7' = '5 lots of 7' + '2 lots of 7'.

Step 1:   5 x 7 = 35
Step 2:   2 x 7 = 14
Add: 7 x 7 = 49

Using the key number fact cards:

$$5 \times 7 = 35$$

+

$$2 \times 7 = 14$$

(35 + 14 = 49)

7 x 7 = 49

8 x 7 = 56   (also 7 x 8 = 56)

Method 1

Based on the key numbers: $8 = 2 \times 2 \times 2$

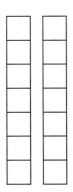 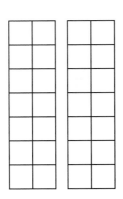 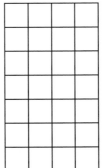 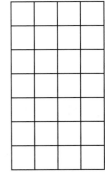

2 x 7 = 14   2 x 14 = 28   2 x 28 = 56

8 x 7 is worked out by using 2x three times:

Step 1:   2 x 7   = 14
Step 2:   2 x 14   = 28
Step 3:   2 x 28   = 56

Method 2

Take 8 x 7 and turn it around into 7 x 8.

     using '7 lots of 8' = '5 lots of 8' + '2 lots of 8'.

Step 1:   5 x 8 = 40
Step 2:   2 x 8 = 16
Add: 7 x 8 = 56

Using the key number fact cards:

$$5 \times 8 = 40$$

$$2 \times 8 = 16$$

$$(40 + 16 = 56)$$

7 x 8 = 56

8 x 7 = 56

9 x 7 = 63   (also 7 x 9 = 63)

9 splits into key numbers: 10 and 1, (note the subtraction): 9 = 10 - 1

'9 lots of 7' = '10 lots of 7' - '1 lot of 7.

Step 1:   10 x 7 = 70
Step 2:   1 x 7 = 7
Subtract: 9 x 7 = 63

Using the key number fact cards:

$$10 \times 7 = 70$$

-   **(subtract)**

$$1 \times 7 = 7$$

(70 – 7 = 63)

9 x 7 = 63

First, don't forget,

Check for 9x facts: the digits in the answer add up to 9.

9 x 7 = 63   6 + 3 = 9

Second, don't forget,

You can use the gypsy (finger) method for any 9x fact.

8 x 8 = 64

8 x 8 is a square, 8^2

A chess (or draughts) board is an 8 x 8 square, there are 64 playing squares.

Repeated multiplication

8 is 2 x 2 x 2

So, 8 x 8 is: 2 x 2 x 2 x 2 x 2 x 2   this means 8 x 8 can be broken down into repeated multiplication involving six twos.

So 8 x 8 can be worked out by repeated multiplication by 2, starting with two of the six twos.

2 x **2** =   4
2 x 4 =   8
2 x 8 = 16
2 x 16 = 32
2 x 32 = 64

There are six twos involved in that repeated multiplication.

8 x 8 = 64

$$9 \times 8 = 72 \qquad \text{(also } 8 \times 9 = 72\text{)}$$

9 splits into key numbers: 10 and 1, (note the subtraction): $9 = 10 - 1$

'9 lots of 8' = '0 lots of 8' - '1 lot of 8'.

Step 1: $10 \times 8 = 80$
Step 2: $\underline{1 \times 8 = 8}$
Subtract: $9 \times 8 = 72$

Using the key number fact cards:

$$10 \times 8 = 80$$

-   **(subtract)**

$$1 \times 8 = 8$$

$(80 - 8 = 72)$

$$\mathbf{9 \times 8 = 72}$$

First, don't forget,

Check for 9x facts: the digits in the answer add up to 9.

$$9 \times 8 = 72 \qquad 7 + 2 = 9$$

Second, don't forget,

You can use the gypsy (finger) method for any 9x fact.

$$9 \times 9 = 81 \qquad \text{(also } 9 \times 9 = 81\text{)}$$

9 splits into key numbers: 10 and 1, (note the subtraction): $9 = 10 - 1$

'9 lots of 9' = '10 lots of 9' – '1 lot of 9'.

Step 1: $10 \times 9 = 90$
Step 2: $\underline{1 \times 9 = 9}$
Subtract: $9 \times 9 = 81$

Using the key number fact cards:

$$10 \times 9 = 90$$

$$-\qquad \text{(subtract)}$$

$$1 \times 9 = 9$$

$$(90 - 9 = 81)$$

$$9 \times 9 = 81$$

First, don't forget,

Check for 9x facts: the digits in the answer add up to 9.

$$9 \times 9 = 81 \qquad 8 + 1 = 9$$

Second, don't forget,

You can use the gypsy (finger) method for any 9x fact.

Conclusion and extension to other facts and calculations

So, what to do next?

Practise, practise, practise!

Use the basic fact cards.

Practise filling in blank number squares.

Use coins to help you 'see' the links and methods.

Don't feel pressured into working quickly at first.
Build up speed, but do not let the demand for speed make you anxious.

Extension: These strategies can be applied to bigger numbers.

For example, working out 12 x 8:

12 splits up into 10 + 2,   12 lots of 8 = 10 lots of 8 + 2 lots of 8.

Step 1:   '10 lots of 8'   10 x 8 = 80
Step 2:   '2 lots of 8'   2 x 8 = 16
Add: '12 lots of 8'   12 x 8 = 96

The splitting up/breaking down into key numbers can be applied to many numbers.

For example,

11x   '10 lots of' plus '1 lot of':   10x add 1x

12x   '10 lots of' plus '2 lots of': 10x add 2x

15x '10 lots of' plus half of 'ten lots of': 10x add ½ x 10x

(For example, 15 x 8 = 80 + 40 = 120)

19x 2 x '10 lots of' minus '1 lot of'

20x 2 x '10 lots of'

50x ½ of '100 lots of'

70x '20 lots of' plus '50 lots of'

Section

3

The times table square

	0	1	2	3	4	5	6	7	8	9	10
0	0	0	0	0	0	0	0	0	0	0	0
1	0	1	2	3	4	5	6	7	8	9	10
2	0	2	4	6	8	10	12	14	16	18	20
3	0	3	6	9	12	15	18	21	24	27	30
4	0	4	8	12	16	20	24	28	32	36	40
5	0	5	10	15	20	25	30	35	40	45	50
6	0	6	12	18	24	30	36	42	48	54	60
7	0	7	14	21	28	35	42	49	56	63	70
8	0	8	16	24	32	40	48	56	64	72	80
9	0	9	18	27	36	45	54	63	72	81	90
10	0	10	20	30	40	50	60	70	80	90	100

Blank times table squares

	0	1	2	3	4	5	6	7	8	9	10
0											
1											
2											
3											
4											
5											
6											
7											
8											
9											
10											

	0	1	2	3	4	5	6	7	8	9	10
0											
1											
2											
3											
4											
5											
6											
7											
8											
9											
10											

	0	1	2	3	4	5	6	7	8	9	10
0											
1											
2											
3											
4											
5											
6											
7											
8											
9											
10											

	0	1	2	3	4	5	6	7	8	9	10
0											
1											
2											
3											
4											
5											
6											
7											
8											
9											
10											

Number strips: 1s, 2s, 5s, 9s, 10s.

Key fact cards

1 x 3 = 3	2 x 3 = 6
5 x 3 = 15	10 x 3 = 30
1 x 4 = 4	2 x 4 = 8
5 x 4 = 20	10 x 4 = 40
1 x 5 = 5	2 x 5 = 10
5 x 5 = 25	10 x 5 = 50

1 x 6 = 6

2 x 6 = 12

5 x 6 = 30

10 x 6 = 60

1 x 7 = 7

2 x 7 = 14

5 x 7 = 35

10 x 7 = 70

1 x 8 = 8

2 x 8 = 16

5 x 8 = 40

10 x 8 = 80

1 x 9 = 9

2 x 9 = 18

5 x 9 = 45

10 x 9 = 90

These are all the facts you need to memorise.

You can use them to work out any other times table fact.

You can photocopy these facts onto card and cut them up.

You can then use them for memorising games such as 'pelmanism', matching any similar or linked facts.

You can use them to work out other facts as has been done throughout Section 2 of this book.

It is often much better to work out what you can't remember than simply remember it, it is more skilful.

GOOD LUCK!